Perform with
Times
Tables

The one-to-one coaching system for
success with multiplication and division

David J Sharp

Copies of this book can be obtained from:

www.123learning.co.uk
Tel/Fax: 0115 919 3911

Perform with Times Tables
ISBN: 978-0-9539812-3-6

Published by Power of 2 Publishing Ltd
Nottingham, England
First published 2008
Printed in UK

Also available:

Plus 1:
The introductory coaching system for maths success
ISBN: 978-0-9539812-1-2

Power of 2:
The one to one coaching system for maths success
ISBN: 978-0-9539812-0-5

Perform with Time:
The one-to-one coaching system for success with time
ISBN: 978-0-9539812-2-9

This book belongs to: ....

Welcome to Perform with Times Tables

This book will enable students to learn the basic multiplication and division facts up to 10 x 10. It will also give the skills to apply this knowledge to other facts. The book is for anyone who benefits from repeated practice and explanation and it stems from the need of some people to have more reinforcement and practice than is often available.

Perform with Times Tables has developed from the success of our previous books. Part of the reason for the huge success of these books is the immense sense of achievement that a person gets when working through the books. This feeling should not be underestimated and therefore this book must be seen as a whole programme of study. It is not intended that certain pages should be used in isolation. A contents page has not been included for this reason. It is intended that everyone should start at the beginning and work through the whole book. Students will also gain a sense of success and confidence.

On each page there is a script for the coach to read, or this could be read by the student. Write down the date you begin each page. There is a space in the bottom left hand corner for this. When each page is completed, record the date in the bottom right hand corner. Please see the worked examples on pages 16 and 17.

Perform with Times Tables has been found to work best when it is used 4 or 5 times a week, with each session lasting for about 10-15 minutes. It is for this reason that we encourage you not to leave it too long between sessions.

Perform with Times Tables

Using this book

Three ticks

Perform with Times Tables requires that each question is answered correctly on three consecutive occasions on different days. When a question is answered correctly, a tick should be placed on the line. If the question is not answered correctly, then a dot should be used instead. When a question has been given three consecutive ticks, that question need not be asked again. If a student has not gained three consecutive ticks for a particular question, by the end of the grid, then that question should be written in the next Recap Grid. The first Recap Grid is on page 27.

Three consecutive ticks are also required on the Recap Grid pages. Please see the examples on pages 16 and 17.

Here are a few ideas that you may find useful when working through *Perform with Times Tables*

Accepting the first answer

It is good for the coach to accept the first answer that is given. This will encourage students to think before answering and to find a suitable method to use. However self-correction by the student should be encouraged and therefore you should use your discretion when wrong answers are self-corrected.

Coaching and helping the student

If any coaching or help is given, do not tick the question on that day. If a wrong answer is offered, put a dot in the box next to the question. If any help is needed to enable the student to complete the calculation, a dot should also be placed next to that question.

Perform with Times Tables

Notes and working out

Throughout *Perform with Times Tables* there is space available for your notes and working out. Both the coach and the student can use this space. Students will find diagrams very helpful to demonstrate different methods that can be used.

"How did you work that out?"

It's good to ask a student "How did you work that out?". Firstly it can reinforce the method that the student uses. Secondly it can encourage students to use mathematical vocabulary. Also there are no answers in this book. Asking how an answer was worked out gives the student (and coach) an opportunity to check that the answer is correct. Space is available in *Perform with Times Tables* to be used by the coach to explain methods and remind students about strategies they can use.

The power of success

Part of the reason for the success of this book is the sense of achievement gained by the students as they work through the pages. Students will get a great deal of pride from seeing their progress. Setting targets for the student to reach by a certain date will also aid the sense of achievement. The power of success should not be underestimated. This feeling of success will be compounded when they see the pages being ticked off. It has been found that using an elastic band to hold the completed pages works well in showing the progress made.

Perform with Times Tables

The Format of the Book

This book has been written to support those students who have struggled to pick up learning their times tables facts. It is not intended to teach the facts to someone meeting them for the first time. For this reason, the book takes a different strategy to the usual one applied.

Firstly, it links all multiplication facts with the corresponding division facts. So whenever 7 x 6 = 42 or 6 x 7 = 42 is mentioned, 42 ÷ 7 = 6 and 42 ÷ 6 = 7 will also be practiced. Secondly, the order which the facts are introduced differs from the usual sequence.

Students are normally taught to learn their times-tables facts starting with the x2 table, moving on to x10 and x5. This is often followed by x3, x4, x6 and x9. Finally, x8 and x7 are learnt. However, many students struggle to keep pace with the new facts which are introduced and don't have the necessary repetition and reinforcement they need.

Whenever tables are re-introduced, it is often in the form of needing to learn a set list of facts linked to one number, such as the 7 times table. This can have the affect of presenting too many unknown facts in one go.

This book represents the tables and division facts in 10 sections.

The first section focuses on all the times tables and corresponding division facts up to 10 x 10 which have an answer between 90 and 100 inclusive. Therefore, the initial parts are
10 x 10 = 100, 9 x 10 = 90, 10 x 9 = 90, 100 ÷ 10 = 10, 90 ÷ 9 = 10, 90 ÷ 10 = 9.

Perform with Times Tables

Approaching the facts in this way enables confidence to be developed while working on a manageable amount of new information.

Following on from this, the times table facts with an answer between 80 and 90 inclusive are looked at. Namely; $9 \times 9 = 81$, $9 \times 10 = 90$, $10 \times 8 = 80$, $81 \div 9 = 9$, $80 \div 8 = 10$, $80 \div 10 = 8$.

This process continues, building up the facts that are known and incorporating valuable repetition and reinforcement. Each new section includes only a few new facts, with the more difficult ones coming relatively early in the book, allowing time for over-learning. Also, the final facts to be introduced will be the ones that the student may already have had more practice with, being mainly from the 2 times table.

This structure of introducing these facts has proved successful for many students. Please do get in touch with us if you have any comments. Our contact details are at the start of the book.

1	2	3	4	5	6	7	8	9	10
2	4	6	8	10	12	14	16	18	20
3	6	9	12	15	18	21	24	27	30
4	8	12	16	20	24	28	32	36	40
5	10	15	20	25	30	35	40	45	50
6	12	18	24	30	36	42	48	54	60
7	14	21	28	35	42	49	56	63	70
8	16	24	32	40	48	56	64	72	80
9	18	27	36	45	54	63	72	81	90
10	20	30	40	50	60	70	80	90	100

Perform with Times Tables

Quick recall

Each student needs to increase the calculations they can do 'without thinking'. If they 'know' certain facts they can then concentrate on other aspects of their maths. Students need regular practice in these skills. Too often students rely on their fingers and counting to do basic calculations. This will hinder their progress. *Perform with Times Tables* allows students to get repeated practice in facts that they need to know to develop their maths. The book also offers a great deal of structured revision, which alongside the 'three ticks', helps to develop learning.

Mental Calculations

Perform with Times Tables is essentially about giving students the skills to deal with multiplication and division in everyday situations. Although students should be encouraged to carry out the calculations in this book without using pen and paper, many of the methods shown will be developed and understood through writing them down. However, students may want to jot down some notes about their work and there is nothing wrong with this, providing the aim is to work towards developing mental calculations.

Perform with Times Tables

Use of equipment
Using practical equipment to help reinforce the concepts in *Perform with Times Tables* is recommended. Such items as counters, blocks, bead-strings, multiplication squares and number lines may be useful in helping students to gain confidence in learning multiplication and division facts.

Games and Activities
In life, maths can be used for enjoyment as well as necessity. Although there are no games in *Perform with Times Tables*, it is important for students to experience activities. There are many resources available which offer a selection of maths games and activities.

We hope you enjoy using *Perform with Times Tables*.

Vocabulary used in this book

Multiply

There are lots of ways of talking about multiplication.

The sum $3 \times 4 = 12$ can be written as:

- 3 times 4 = 12
- 3 multiplied by 4 = 12
- 3 lots of 4 are 12
- the product of 3 and 4 is 12
- 3 sets of 4 are 12
- three fours are twelve

Division

There are a number of ways to write division.

$18 \div 3 = 6$ can be written as:

- 18 divided by 3 = 6
- 18 shared by 3 = 6
- $\dfrac{18}{3} = 6$
- $3 \overline{)18}$ with quotient 6

The mathematical terms for a division are

$$18 \div 3 = 6$$

dividend divisor quotient

lots of
2 lots of 5 are 10
2 x 5 = 10

multiplied by
3 multiplied by 4 = 12
3 x 4 = 12

divided by
12 divided by 3 is 4
12 ÷ 3 = 4

X

sets of
3 sets of 3 are 9
3 x 3 = 9

÷

groups of
4 groups of 2 are 8
4 x 2 = 8

times
4 times 4 = 16
4 x 4 =16

shared by
15 shared by 3 is 5
15 ÷ 3 = 5

Some notes about Multiplication and Division

This book focuses on enabling students to learn the basic multiplication and division facts up to 10 x 10. This will then enable them to apply this knowledge to other facts.

Features of Multiplication and Division
Three different ways of thinking about multiplication are:

as repeated addition, for example 3 + 3 + 3 + 3 + 3;

as a grouping, for example five rows of four objects;
5 lots of 4 • • • •
          • • • •
          • • • •
          • • • •
          • • • •

as a scaling factor, for example making a line three times longer.

The use of the multiplication sign can cause difficulties. Strictly, 3 x 4 means 3 multiplied by 4 or four 'lots of' three. This is counter to the intuitive way of interpreting 3 x 4, which is often thought of as three lots of four. Fortunately, multiplication is commutative, 3 x 4 being equal to 4 x 3, so the outcome is the same. The colloquial use of 'three times four' provides another confusion: a phrase that was derived, presumably, from the idea of 'three, taken four times ' – or four taken three times.

When multiplication and addition or subtraction are combined, as in 3 x (4 + 5), the fact that 3 x (4 + 5) = (3 x 4) + (3 x 5), can be useful in mental calculation.

Division and multiplication are inverse operations. However, whereas any two whole numbers can be multiplied to make another whole number, this is not always the case for division. 12÷4 gives a whole number, but 12÷5 does not. For mental calculation it is important to know multiplication facts in order that the related division facts can be worked out.

Some multiplication methods

There are many different methods you can try. Choose what works best for you. Here are some examples.

Reverse the question
If someone asks you what 3 x 8 is and you're not sure of your 8 times table, turn it around into 8 x 3.

Use the facts you know well, like 10 times a number.
If you need to work out 12 x 4, start with 10 x 4 = 40 and add 2 more 4s to give 48.

Doubling
Doubling is a good trick. If you know that 4 x 4 = 16, then you can work out 8 x 4 by doubling 16, which gives 32.

Separate and add up
If you had to work out 25 x 5 you could use:
10 x 5 = 50 plus another 10 x 5 = 50.
Then 5 x 5 = 25.
Added together 50 + 50 + 25 = 125

Do students need to know their tables?

This book has been written in the belief that if students know their multiplication and division facts, it will allow them to access other areas of the curriculum.

There is a school of thought which says that if students understand the concept behind multiplication and division they will be able to work out the facts as and when they need them. By using this book, students will become confident in quick recall of the multiplication and division facts. This will enable them to use this knowledge to work out other questions or apply their skills to areas such as algebra or shape and space.

Perform with Times Tables

For this section, you need to read out the whole statement,

For example,

$8 \times 8 = \square$

You say $8 \times 8 = 64$

example

Remember, you need to get three consecutive ticks

Read out the following statements:

$8 \times 8 = \square$	✓	•	•	✓	✓	✓	
$7 \times 9 = \square$	•	✓	✓	✓			
$10 \times 6 = \square$	✓	✓	•	✓	✓	✓	
$9 \times \square = 63$	•	✓	✓	✓			
$64 \div 8 = \square$	✓	✓	✓				
$6 \times \square = 60$	•	✓	✓	•	✓	✓	✓
8 lots of 8 equals $\square$	•	•	✓	✓	•	✓	✓
$60 \div 10 = \square$	✓	✓	✓				
64 divided by 8 equals $\square$	•	✓	✓	✓			
$63 \div 9 = \square$	•	•	✓	•	✓	✓	✓
$60 \div \square = 10$	•	•	•	✓	•	•	✓
9 multiplied by 7 equals $\square$	•	✓	✓	✓			

Page 16 started on: 26/1/2019

Page 16 finished on: 2/2/2019

Recap grid

Use this grid to put in any questions you have found difficult so far.

You can put in the questions you found hard or you can make up your own.

example

Remember, you need to get three consecutive ticks

8 lots of 8 equals ☐	✓	✓	•	✓	✓	✓	
60 ÷ ☐ = 10	•	•	✓	•	✓	✓	✓

Page 17 started on: 3/2/2019

Page 17 finished on: 13/2/2019

The **first section** will focus on these facts:

$10 \times 10 = 100$ $9 \times 10 = 90$

$100 \div 10 = 10$ $10 \times 9 = 90$

$90 \div 9 = 10$

$90 \div 10 = 9$

Perform with Times Tables

For this section, you need to read out the whole statement,

For example,

$9 \times 10 = \square$

You say 9 x 10 = 90

Remember, you need to get three consecutive ticks

Read out the following statements:

$9 \times 10 = \square$								
$10 \times 10 = \square$								
$90 \div 9 = \square$								
$100 \div 10 = \square$								
$10 \times \square = 90$								
$\square \div 10 = 9$								
10 lots of 9 equals $\square$								
90 divided by 9 equals $\square$								
9 multiplied by 10 equals $\square$								
$10 \times \square = 100$								
100 divided by 10 equals $\square$								
$10 \times \square = 90$								

The Nine Times Table

This is the nine times table:

$0 \times 9 = 0$

$1 \times 9 = 9$

$2 \times 9 = 18$

$3 \times 9 = 27$

$4 \times 9 = 36$ ⟵ $3+6=9$

$5 \times 9 = 45$

$6 \times 9 = 54$ ⟵ $5+4=9$

$7 \times 9 = 63$

$8 \times 9 = 72$ ⟵ $7+2=9$

$9 \times 9 = 81$

$10 \times 9 = 90$

These numbers increase | These numbers decrease

The nine times table has a number of patterns to help you remember it.

The 2 digits always add up to 9. So,

Also, there is the pattern of the digits decreasing in the units column and increasing in the tens column.

The Nine Times Table

This is a method to work out the nine times table:

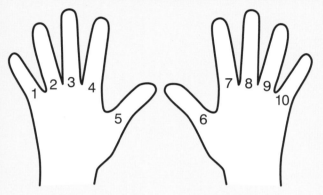

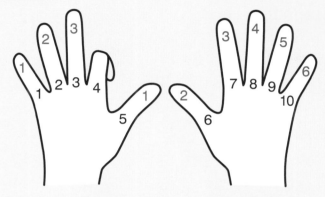

Number the digits of your hands from left to right, as shown above.

Bend the finger of the number you wish to multiply by. For example, 4 x 9. The fourth finger must be bent, as shown above.

Count the digits to the left of the bent finger (as shown by the green numbers) = 3. Count the digits to the right = 6. These are the digits of the product. For example, 3 and 6, so 4 x 9 = 36.

The **second section** will focus on these facts:

$9 \times 9 = 81$ $\qquad$ $8 \times 10 = 80$

$81 \div 9 = 9$ $\qquad$ $10 \times 8 = 80$

$\qquad\qquad\qquad$ $80 \div 8 = 10$

$\qquad\qquad\qquad$ $80 \div 10 = 8$

Perform with Times Tables

For this section, you need to read out the whole statement,

For example,

$9 \times 9 = \square$

You say $9 \times 9 = 81$

*Remember,
you need to get three
consecutive ticks*

Read out the following statements:

$9 \times 9 = \square$							
$8 \times 10 = \square$							
$81 \div 9 = \square$							
$80 \div 8 = \square$							
10 lots of 8 equals $\square$							
$80 \div \square = 8$							
$9 \times \square = 81$							
8 multiplied by 10 equals $\square$							
80 divided by 10 equals $\square$							
81 divided by 9 equals $\square$							
$10 \times \square = 80$							
80 divided by 8 equals $\square$							

The Eight Times Table

This is the eight times table:

0 x 8 = 0
1 x 8 = 8
2 x 8 = 16
3 x 8 = 24
4 x 8 = 32
5 x 8 = 40
6 x 8 = 48
7 x 8 = 56
8 x 8 = 64
9 x 8 = 72
10 x 8 = 80

The numbers in the 8 times table are always even. That means they can be divided by 2 without a remainder. If it's an **odd** number then it is not in the 8 times table!

The unit digits have a regular pattern - they go down in 2s.

1 x 8 = 8 ⟵ 8
2 x 8 = 16   6
3 x 8 = 24   4
4 x 8 = 32   2
5 x 8 = 40   0
6 x 8 = 48 ⟵ 8
7 x 8 = 56   6
8 x 8 = 64   4
9 x 8 = 72   2
10 x 8 = 80   0

A rhyme to help you remember...

He ate and he ate and he sticks in the door, eight times eight is sixty-four

The Eight Times Table

One way to work out answers for the eight times table is to take the two times table then **double** and **double** again.

For example,
to work out 6 x 8

If you know 6 x 2 = 12
Double   =   6 x 4 = 24
Double   =   6 x 8 = 48

Double   Double

1 x 2 = 2	1 x 4 = 4	1 x 8 = 8
2 x 2 = 4	2 x 4 = 8	2 x 8 = 16
3 x 2 = 6	3 x 4 = 12	3 x 8 = 24
4 x 2 = 8	4 x 4 = 16	4 x 8 = 32
5 x 2 = 10	5 x 4 = 20	5 x 8 = 40
6 x 2 = 12	6 x 4 = 24	6 x 8 = 48
7 x 2 = 14	7 x 4 = 28	7 x 8 = 56
8 x 2 = 16	8 x 4 = 32	8 x 8 = 64
9 x 2 = 18	9 x 4 = 36	9 x 8 = 72
10 x 2 = 20	10 x 4 = 40	10 x 8 = 80

Use this space for your notes and working out

Recap grid

Use this grid to put in any questions you have found difficult so far.

You can put in the questions you found hard or you can make up your own.

Remember, you need to get three consecutive ticks

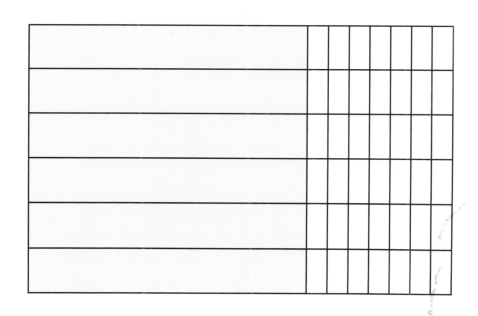

Perform with Times Tables

Use this space for your notes and working out

Recap 90 - 100 facts

For this section, you need to read out the whole statement,

For example, **9 x 10 =** ☐

You say 9 x 10 = 90

Read out the following statements:

10 x ☐ = 100									
90 divided by 9 equals ☐									
90 ÷ 9 = ☐									
9 x ☐ = 90									
☐ ÷ 10 = 9									
100 ÷ 10 = ☐									
10 lots of 9 equals ☐									

This is the ten times table, up to 10 x 10:

$$0 \times 10 = 0$$
$$1 \times 10 = 10$$
$$2 \times 10 = 20$$
$$3 \times 10 = 30$$
$$4 \times 10 = 40$$
$$5 \times 10 = 50$$
$$6 \times 10 = 60$$
$$7 \times 10 = 70$$
$$8 \times 10 = 80$$
$$9 \times 10 = 90$$
$$10 \times 10 = 100$$

This is the next group of facts:

$7 \times 10 = 70$ $9 \times 8 = 72$

$10 \times 7 = 70$ $8 \times 9 = 72$

$70 \div 10 = 7$ $72 \div 9 = 8$

$70 \div 7 = 10$ $72 \div 8 = 9$

Perform with Times Tables

For this section, you need to read out the whole statement,

For example,

$9 \times 8 = \square$

You say $9 \times 8 = 72$

Remember, you need to get three consecutive ticks

Read out the following statements:

$9 \times 8 = \square$							
$10 \times 7 = \square$							
$72 \div 9 = \square$							
$70 \div 7 = \square$							
$7 \times \square = 70$							
$72 \div \square = 9$							
9 multiplied by 8 equals $\square$							
7 lots of 10 = $\square$							
$70 \div 10 = \square$							
$\square \times 9 = 72$							
72 divided by 8 equals $\square$							
10 multiplied by 7 equals $\square$							

Fact Families

Fact families are groups of numbers which can link together to make statements.

An example of a fact-family is 8 10 80.
Using x and ÷, four different facts can
be made:

$80 \div 8 = 10$
$80 \div 10 = 8$
$8 \times 10 = 80$
$10 \times 8 = 80$

With the numbers 9 81 9 only 2 different
facts can be made up:

$9 \times 9 = 81$
$81 \div 9 = 9$

Fact Families

Write in the facts that link with the family of numbers. Write a different fact in each box.

9 10 90

72 8 9

9 81 9

8 10 80

10 10 100

10 7 70

The Seven Times Table

This is the seven times table:

$0 \times 7 = 0$
$1 \times 7 = 7$
$2 \times 7 = 14$
$3 \times 7 = 21$
$4 \times 7 = 28$
$5 \times 7 = 35$
$6 \times 7 = 42$
$7 \times 7 = 49$
$8 \times 7 = 56$
$9 \times 7 = 63$
$10 \times 7 = 70$

There is no easy way to find out if a number is in the 7 times table.

But there is a way of remembering 7×8:

$7 \times 8 = 56$. Just remember - 5, 6, 7, 8.

Try reversing a sum if you are having problems.

$7 \times 5 = 35$
$5 \times 7 = 35$

Recap 80 - 90 facts

For this section, you need to read out the whole statement,

For example,

$8 \times 10 = \square$

You say $8 \times 10 = 80$

Read out the following statements:

$81 \div \square = 9$							
$8 \times 10 = \square$							
$80 \div \square = 10$							
9 times 9 equals $\square$							
$\square \div 10 = 8$							
$8 \times \square = 80$							
$\square \div 9 = 9$							

These are the next group of facts to be introduced:

$6 \times 10 = 60$	$8 \times 8 = 64$	$7 \times 9 = 63$
$10 \times 6 = 60$	$64 \div 8 = 8$	$9 \times 7 = 63$
$60 \div 10 = 6$		$63 \div 9 = 7$
$60 \div 6 = 10$		$63 \div 7 = 9$

Perform with Times Tables

For this section, you need to read out the whole statement,

For example,

$8 \times 8 = \square$

You say $8 \times 8 = 64$

Remember, you need to get three consecutive ticks

Read out the following statements:

$8 \times 8 = \square$								
$7 \times 9 = \square$								
$10 \times 6 = \square$								
$9 \times \square = 63$								
$64 \div 8 = \square$								
$6 \times \square = 60$								
8 lots of 8 equals $\square$								
$60 \div 10 = \square$								
64 divided by 8 equals $\square$								
$63 \div 9 = \square$								
$60 \div \square = 10$								
9 multiplied by 7 equals $\square$								

Use this space for your notes and working out

For this section, you need to read out the whole statement,

For example, **9 x 8 =** ☐

You say 9 x 8 = 72

Read out the following statements:

9 x 8 = ☐							
70 divided by ☐ equals 10							
72 ÷ 9 = ☐							
☐ x 9 = 72							
7 x 10 = ☐							
☐ ÷ 8 = 9							
10 x ☐ = 70							

The Six Times Table

This is the six times table:

0 x 6 = 0
1 x 6 = 6
2 x 6 = 12
3 x 6 = 18
4 x 6 = 24
5 x 6 = 30
6 x 6 = 36
7 x 6 = 42
8 x 6 = 48
9 x 6 = 54
10 x 6 = 60

There is no easy way to find out if a number is in the 6 times table, but here are some tips:

All the numbers in the 6 times table are **even** - they end with either 0, 2, 4, 6 or 8.

They are all a **multiple of 3**.

The Six Times Table

The six times table can be worked out from the 3 times table.

For example,
to work out 6 x 4

If you know 3 x 4 = 12
Double   6 x 4 = 24

Double

3 times table	6 times table
1 x 3 = 3	1 x 6 = 6
2 x 3 = 6	2 x 6 = 12
3 x 3 = 9	3 x 6 = 18
4 x 3 = 12	4 x 6 = 24
5 x 3 = 15	5 x 6 = 30
6 x 3 = 18	6 x 6 = 36
7 x 3 = 21	7 x 6 = 42
8 x 3 = 24	8 x 6 = 48
9 x 3 = 27	9 x 6 = 54
10 x 3 = 30	10 x 6 = 60

Fact Families

Write in the facts that link with the family of numbers. Write a different fact in each box.

7 9 63

10 6 60

6 54 9

8 64 8

8 7 56

5 10 50

Extended Problems

You can use the facts you know to help you work out other types of problems.

These problems include addition or subtraction, as well as multiplication or division.

With these problems you must always work out the multiplication or division part first.

For example,

$9 \times 10 + 1 = \square$

$9 \times 10 = 90$

$\qquad 90 + 1 = \square$

You say $9 \times 10 + 1 = 91$

Read out the following statements:

$9 \times 10 + 1 = \square$								
$10 \times 7 + 2 = \square$								
$9 \times 8 - 2 = \square$								
$100 \div 10 + 5 = \square$								
$8 \times 10 + 3 = \square$								
$9 \times 10 + \square = 93$								
$9 \times 9 + 4 = \square$								
$90 \div 9 + 1 = \square$								
$10 \times 10 - \square = 99$								
$90 \div 10 + 1 = \square$								
$72 \div 8 + \square = 11$								
$70 \div 10 + 1 = \square$								

This section will introduce these facts:

$5 \times 10 = 50$	$6 \times 9 = 54$	$7 \times 8 = 56$
$10 \times 5 = 50$	$9 \times 6 = 54$	$8 \times 7 = 56$
$50 \div 10 = 5$	$54 \div 9 = 6$	$56 \div 8 = 7$
$50 \div 5 = 10$	$54 \div 6 = 9$	$56 \div 7 = 8$

Perform with Times Tables

For this section, you need to read out the whole statement,

For example,

$6 \times 9 = \square$

You say $6 \times 9 = 54$

*Remember,
you need to get three
consecutive ticks*

Read out the following statements:

$6 \times 9 = \square$								
$8 \times 7 = \square$								
$5 \times 10 = \square$								
$54 \div 9 = \square$								
$50 \div 10 = \square$								
$7 \times 8 = \square$								
$9 \times \square = 54$								
56 divided by 7 equals $\square$								
$\square \div 5 = 10$								
$54 \div 6 = \square$								
$56 \div \square = 7$								
$10 \times 5 = \square$								

Use this space for your notes and working out

Recap 60 - 70 facts

For this section, you need to read out the whole statement,

For example, **7 x 9 =** ☐

You say 7 x 9 = 63

Read out the following statements:

7 x 9 = ☐								
☐ ÷ 8 = 8								
60 divided by 10 equals ☐								
☐ x 10 = 60								
9 multiplied by ☐ equals 63								
63 ÷ 9 = ☐								
8 x 8 = ☐								

Perform with Times Tables

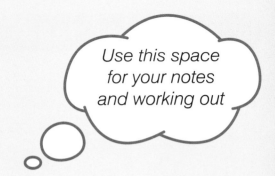

Use this space for your notes and working out

The Five Times Table

This is the five times table:

0 x 5 = 0
1 x 5 = 5
2 x 5 = 10
3 x 5 = 15
4 x 5 = 20
5 x 5 = 25
6 x 5 = 30
7 x 5 = 35
8 x 5 = 40
9 x 5 = 45
10 x 5 = 50

All multiples of 5 end in a 5 or a 0.

So 4,320 is in the 5 times table because it ends in a 0.

55,552 is not because it ends in a 2.

Recap 90 - 100 facts

For this section, you need to read out the whole statement,

For example, $\square$ x 10 = 100

You say 10 x 10 = 100

Read out the following statements:

$\square$ x 10 = 100							
90 ÷ 9 = $\square$							
100 ÷ $\square$ = 10							
10 times $\square$ equals 90							
90 divided by 10 equals $\square$							
9 x $\square$ = 90							
10 x 10 = $\square$							

Page 50 started on: ....

Recap 80 - 90 facts

For this section, you need to read out the whole statement,

For example, 10 x $\square$ = 80

You say 10 x 8 = 80

Read out the following statements:

10 x $\square$ = 80							
9 x $\square$ = 81							
$\square$ ÷ 8 = 10							
81 divided by 9 equals $\square$							
8 multiplied by 10 equals $\square$							
80 ÷ 10 = $\square$							
$\square$ x 8 = 80							

Page 50 finished on: ....

Recap 70 - 80 facts

For this section, you need to read out the whole statement,

For example, **8 x 9** = ☐

You say 8 x 9 = 72

Read out the following statements:

8 x 9 = ☐							
10 x ☐ = 70							
☐ ÷ 9 = 8							
☐ x 10 = 70							
72 divided by 8 equals ☐							
70 ÷ 7 = ☐							
☐ x 8 = 72							

Page 51 started on: ....

Recap 60 - 70 facts

For this section, you need to read out the whole statement,

For example, **63 ÷ 9** = ☐

You say 63 ÷ 9 = 7

Read out the following statements:

63 ÷ 9 = ☐							
8 x 8 = ☐							
☐ ÷ 6 = 10							
7 times 9 equals ☐							
10 x ☐ = 60							
☐ ÷ 8 = 8							
☐ divided by 7 equals 9							

Page 51 finished on: ....

Fact Families

Write in the facts that link with the family of numbers. Write a different fact in each box.

4 10 40

6 8 48

6 42 7

7 49 7

9 45 5

5 40 8

Extended Problems

You can use the facts you know to help you work out other types of problems.

These problems include addition or subtraction, as well as multiplication or division.

With these problems you must always work out the multiplication or division part first.

For example,

$6 \times 10 + 1 = \square$

$6 \times 10 = 60$

$\qquad 60 + 1 = \square$

You say $6 \times 10 + 1 = 61$

Read out the following statements:

$6 \times 10 + 1 = \square$								
$54 \div 9 + 1 = \square$								
$5 \times 10 - 2 = \square$								
$64 \div 8 + 2 = \square$								
$7 \times 8 + 1 = \square$								
$8 \times 8 + 1 = \square$								
$63 \div 7 - 3 = \square$								
$9 \times 6 + 4 = \square$								
$10 \times 5 + \square = 53$								
$8 \times 7 + \square = 58$								
$10 \times 6 + 5 = \square$								
$50 \div 10 + 2 = \square$								

This section will introduce these facts:

$4 \times 10 = 40$ $6 \times 7 = 42$ $9 \times 5 = 45$ $8 \times 6 = 48$ $7 \times 7 = 49$

$10 \times 4 = 40$ $7 \times 6 = 42$ $5 \times 9 = 45$ $6 \times 8 = 48$ $49 \div 7 = 7$

$40 \div 10 = 4$ $42 \div 7 = 6$ $45 \div 9 = 5$ $48 \div 6 = 8$

$40 \div 4 = 10$ $42 \div 6 = 7$ $45 \div 5 = 9$ $48 \div 8 = 6$

Perform with Times Tables

For this section, you need to read out the whole statement,

For example,

$4 \times 10 = \square$

You say $4 \times 10 = 40$

> *Remember, you need to get three consecutive ticks*

Read out the following statements:

$4 \times 10 = \square$								
$40 \div 4 = \square$								
$6 \times 7 = \square$								
$9 \times 5 = \square$								
$42 \div 6 = \square$								
$45 \div 9 = \square$								
$8 \times 6 = \square$								
$7 \times 7 = \square$								
$48 \div 6 = \square$								
$49 \div 7 = \square$								
$6 \times 8 = \square$								
$40 \div 10 = \square$								

Perform with Times Tables

Use this space for your notes and working out

Perform with Times Tables

For this section, you need to read out the whole statement,

For example,

7 x 7 = ☐

You say 7 x 7 = 49

Remember, you need to get three consecutive ticks

Read out the following statements:

7 x 7 = ☐								
48 ÷ 8 = ☐								
5 x 9 = ☐								
6 x 7 = ☐								
45 ÷ 5 = ☐								
42 ÷ 6 = ☐								
49 ÷ 7 = ☐								
6 multiplied by 8 equals ☐								
45 divided by 9 equals ☐								
4 x ☐ = 40								
7 multiplied by 6 equals ☐								
40 divided by 4 equals ☐								

This is the four times table:

0 x 4 = 0
1 x 4 = 4
2 x 4 = 8
3 x 4 = 12
4 x 4 = 16
5 x 4 = 20
6 x 4 = 24
7 x 4 = 28
8 x 4 = 32
9 x 4 = 36
10 x 4 = 40

All the numbers in the 4 times table are **even** - they end with 0, 2, 4, 6 or 8.

To find out if a number is a multiple of 4, look at the last 2 digits of the number. If they are a multiple of 4, then the whole number is.

Let's look at the number 116. This is a multiple of 4 because 16 is in the 4 times table.

The Four Times Table

The 4 times table can be worked out from the 2 times table.

For example,
to work out 7 x 4

If you know 7 x 2 = 14
Double   7 x 4 = 28

Double

1 x 2 = 2	1 x 4 = 4
2 x 2 = 4	2 x 4 = 8
3 x 2 = 6	3 x 4 = 12
4 x 2 = 8	4 x 4 = 16
5 x 2 = 10	5 x 4 = 20
6 x 2 = 12	6 x 4 = 24
7 x 2 = 14	7 x 4 = 28
8 x 2 = 16	8 x 4 = 32
9 x 2 = 18	9 x 4 = 36
10 x 2 = 20	10 x 4 = 40

Use this space for your notes and working out

Recap grid

Use this grid to put in any questions you have found difficult so far.

You can put in the questions you found hard or you can make up your own.

Remember, you need to get three consecutive ticks

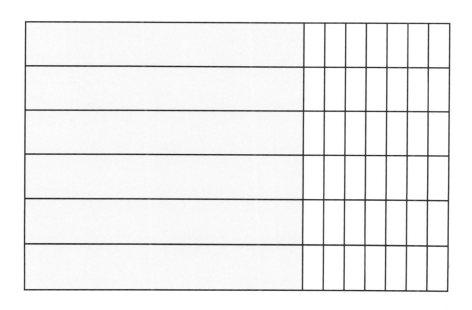

This is the next group of facts to be introduced:

$3 \times 10 = 30$ $6 \times 6 = 36$ $7 \times 5 = 35$

$10 \times 3 = 30$ $36 \div 6 = 6$ $5 \times 7 = 35$

$30 \div 10 = 3$ $35 \div 5 = 7$

$30 \div 3 = 10$ $35 \div 7 = 5$

Perform with Times Tables

For this section, you need to read out the whole statement,

For example,

$3 \times 10 = \square$

You say $3 \times 10 = 30$

Remember, you need to get three consecutive ticks

Read out the following statements:

$3 \times 10 = \square$								
$6 \times 6 = \square$								
$7 \times 5 = \square$								
$30 \div 3 = \square$								
35 divided by 7 $= \square$								
$35 \div \square = 7$								
10 multiplied by 3 $= \square$								
$36 \div 6 = \square$								
$5 \times 7 = \square$								
$30 \div \square = 3$								
$7 \times \square = 35$								
6 times 6 equals $\square$								

The Three Times Table

This is the three times table:

0 x 3 = 0
1 x 3 = 3
2 x 3 = 6
3 x 3 = 9
4 x 3 = 12
5 x 3 = 15
6 x 3 = 18
7 x 3 = 21
8 x 3 = 24
9 x 3 = 27
10 x 3 = 30

The Three Times Table

To find out if a number is in the 3 times table, add up its digits. If they add up to 3, 6, or 9, then you know that it's in the 3 times table.

Let's look at 15.
The digits are 1 and 5.

Add these together and you get 6.
$1 + 5 = 6$.

So 15 is in the 3 times table.

Now let's look at a bigger number, 156.
The digits are 1, 5 and 6.

Add $1 + 5 + 6$ and you get 12.

Now add up the digits 1 and 2 and you get 3. So 156 is in the 3 times table.

It always works, even with a really big number like 12,346,911.

Just add up the digits:
$1 + 2 + 3 + 4 + 6 + 9 + 1 + 1 = 27$.

Then add $2 + 7 = 9$.
So 12,346,911 is in the 3 times table.

Recap 50 - 60 facts

For this section, you need to read out the whole statement,

For example, **10 x 5 =** ☐

You say 10 x 5 = 50

Read out the following statements:

10 x 5 = ☐							
9 x ☐ = 54							
☐ divided by 5 equals 10							
☐ x 8 = 56							
56 ÷ 7 = ☐							
☐ ÷ 6 = 9							
8 x 7 = ☐							

Recap 40 - 50 facts

For this section, you need to read out the whole statement,

For example, **10 x $\square$ = 40**

You say 10 x 4 = 40

Read out the following statements:

10 x $\square$ = 40							
6 multiplied by 7 equals $\square$							
$\square$ x 9 = 45							
48 ÷ $\square$ = 8							
7 x 7 = $\square$							
42 divided by 6 equals $\square$							
40 ÷ 4 = $\square$							

Fact Families

Write in the facts that link with the family of numbers. Write a different fact in each box.

30 3 10

9 4 36

30 5 6

6 6 36

35 7 5

32 8 4

Extended Problems

You can use the facts you know to help you work out other types of problems.

These problems include addition or subtraction, as well as multiplication or division.

With these problems you must always work out the multiplication or division part first.

For example,

$4 \times 10 + 1 = \boxed{}$

$4 \times 10 = 40$

$\qquad 40 + 1 = \boxed{}$

You say $4 \times 10 + 1 = 41$

Read out the following statements:

$4 \times 10 + 1 = \boxed{}$							
$9 \times 5 - 1 = \boxed{}$							
$8 \times 5 + 3 = \boxed{}$							
$6 \times 7 + 2 = \boxed{}$							
$8 \times 6 + \boxed{} = 50$							
$45 \div 9 + 1 = \boxed{}$							
$40 \div 4 + \boxed{} = 12$							
$42 \div 6 + 3 = \boxed{}$							
$5 \times 8 + \boxed{} = 42$							
$7 \times 7 + 1 = \boxed{}$							
$7 \times 6 + \boxed{} = 45$							
$49 \div 7 + 3 = \boxed{}$							

This section will introduce these facts:

$2 \times 10 = 20$	$5 \times 5 = 25$	$7 \times 3 = 21$	$8 \times 3 = 24$	$6 \times 4 = 24$	$9 \times 3 = 27$
$10 \times 2 = 20$	$25 \div 5 = 5$	$3 \times 7 = 21$	$3 \times 8 = 24$	$4 \times 6 = 24$	$3 \times 9 = 27$
$20 \div 10 = 2$		$21 \div 3 = 7$	$24 \div 3 = 8$	$24 \div 4 = 6$	$27 \div 3 = 9$
$20 \div 2 = 10$		$21 \div 7 = 3$	$24 \div 8 = 3$	$24 \div 6 = 4$	$27 \div 9 = 3$

Perform with Times Tables

For this section, you need to read out the whole statement,

For example,

$5 \times 5 = \square$

You say $5 \times 5 = 25$

Remember, you need to get three consecutive ticks

Read out the following statements:

$5 \times 5 = \square$							
$7 \times 3 = \square$							
$3 \times 9 = \square$							
$8 \times 3 = \square$							
2 lots of 10 equals $\square$							
$4 \times 6 = \square$							
$25 \div 5 = \square$							
3 multiplied by $\square$ equals 21							
24 divided by 6 equals $\square$							
$20 \div 2 = \square$							
21 divided by 3 equals $\square$							
$\square \times 2 = 20$							

Use this space for your notes and working out

Perform with Times Tables

For this section, you need to read out the whole statement,

For example,

$9 \times 3 = \square$

You say $9 \times 3 = 27$

Remember, you need to get three consecutive ticks

Read out the following statements:

$9 \times 3 = \square$								
$3 \times \square = 24$								
21 divided by 7 equals $\square$								
$27 \div \square = 9$								
$5 \times 5 = \square$								
6 multiplied by 4 equals $\square$								
27 divided by 9 equals $\square$								
$24 \div 3 = \square$								
24 divided by 4 equals $\square$								
$8 \times 3 = \square$								
24 divided by 8 equals $\square$								
$20 \div 10 = \square$								

This is the two times table:

$0 \times 2 = 0$
$1 \times 2 = 2$
$2 \times 2 = 4$
$3 \times 2 = 6$
$4 \times 2 = 8$
$5 \times 2 = 10$
$6 \times 2 = 12$
$7 \times 2 = 14$
$8 \times 2 = 16$
$9 \times 2 = 18$
$10 \times 2 = 20$

All the numbers in the 2 times table are **even**, they end with either 0, 2, 4, 6 or 8.

To find out if a number is in the 2 times table, look at the digit at the end. 1,357,318 is a multiple of 2 because the digit at the end is 8, which is even.

Multiplying a number by 2 is the same as **doubling** it. Double 6 is the same as 6 x 2, which equals 12.

Dividing a number by 2 is the same as **halving** it. Half of 10 is the same as 10 ÷ 2 which equals 5.

The answers of the 2 times table are all even numbers

Recap grid

Use this grid to put in any questions you have found difficult so far.

You can put in the questions you found hard or you can make up your own.

Remember, you need to get three consecutive ticks

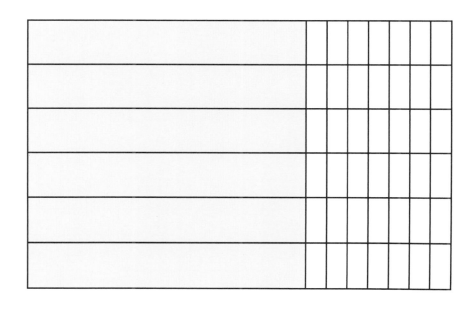

Recap 30 - 40 facts

For this section, you need to read out the whole statement,

For example, **5 x 7 =** ☐

You say 5 x 7 = 35

Read out the following statements:

5 x 7 = ☐						
10 x ☐ = 30						
35 ÷ ☐ = 5						
☐ multiplied by 7 equals 35						
☐ divided by 3 equals 10						
6 x 6 = ☐						
36 divided by 6 equals ☐						

Page **76** started on: ....

Recap 20 - 30 facts

For this section, you need to read out the whole statement,

For example, **7 x 3 =** ☐

You say 7 x 3 = 21

Read out the following statements:

7 x 3 = ☐						
5 times by 5 equals ☐						
21 divided by 3 equals ☐						
☐ x 3 = 24						
24 ÷ 4 = ☐						
☐ ÷ 3 = 9						
9 x 3 = ☐						

Page **76** finished on: ....

Recap mixed 70 - 100 facts

For this section, you need to read out the whole statement,

For example, **9 x 9 =** ☐

You say 9 x 9 = 81

Read out the following statements:

9 x 9 = ☐							
90 ÷ 9 = ☐							
9 times 8 equals ☐							
70 ÷ 10 = ☐							
81 ÷ 9 = ☐							
80 divided by 10 equals ☐							
8 x ☐ = 72							

Page **77** started on: ....

Recap mixed 40 - 70 facts

For this section, you need to read out the whole statement,

For example, **7 x 9 =** ☐

You say 7 x 9 = 63

Read out the following statements:

7 x 9 = ☐							
8 times 8 equals ☐							
6 multiplied by ☐ equals 54							
45 ÷ 5 = ☐							
8 multiplied by 6 equals ☐							
☐ divided by 7 equals 7							
7 x 6 = ☐							

Page **77** finished on: ....

Fact Families

Write in the facts that link with the family of
numbers. Write a different fact in each box.

3 27 9

10 2 20

28 7 4

8 3 24

21 3 7

5 25 5

Extended Problems

You can use the facts you know to help you work out other types of problems.

These problems include addition or subtraction, as well as multiplication or division.

With these problems you must always work out the multiplication or division part first.

For example,

$3 \times 10 + 1 = \square$

$3 \times 10 = 30$

$\qquad 30 + 1 = \square$

You say $3 \times 10 + 1 = 31$

Read out the following statements:

$3 \times 10 + 1 = \square$								
$9 \times 4 + 4 = \square$								
$8 \times 4 - 2 = \square$								
$7 \times 5 + \square = 36$								
$5 \times 6 + 4 = \square$								
$6 \times 6 - 3 = \square$								
$6 \times 5 - 1 = \square$								
$35 \div 5 + 2 = \square$								
$32 \div 8 + \square = 5$								
$4 \times 9 - 1 = \square$								
$30 \div 10 + \square = 5$								
$10 \times 3 + \square = 33$								

This section covers these facts:

$7 \times 2 = 14$	$5 \times 3 = 15$	$9 \times 3 = 27$	$2 \times 8 = 16$	$9 \times 2 = 18$	$4 \times 4 = 16$
$2 \times 7 = 14$	$3 \times 5 = 15$	$3 \times 9 = 27$	$8 \times 2 = 16$	$2 \times 9 = 18$	$16 \div 4 = 4$
$14 \div 2 = 7$	$15 \div 3 = 5$	$27 \div 3 = 9$	$16 \div 8 = 2$	$18 \div 2 = 9$	
$14 \div 7 = 2$	$15 \div 5 = 3$	$27 \div 9 = 3$	$16 \div 2 = 8$	$18 \div 9 = 2$	

Perform with Times Tables

For this section, you need to read out the whole statement,

For example,

$5 \times 3 = \square$

You say $5 \times 3 = 15$

Remember, you need to get three consecutive ticks

Read out the following statements:

$5 \times 3 = \square$								
$2 \times 7 = \square$								
$15 \div 3 = \square$								
$3 \times 9 = \square$								
$\square \times 9 = 18$								
$3 \times \square = 15$								
$14 \div 2 = \square$								
$16 \div \square = 8$								
$4 \times \square = 16$								
$2 \times 8 = \square$								
$27 \div 9 = \square$								
$9 \times 2 = \square$								

Use this space for your notes and working out

Perform with Times Tables

For this section, you need to read out the whole statement,

For example,

4 x 4 = ☐

You say 4 x 4 = 16

Remember, you need to get three consecutive ticks

Read out the following statements:

4 x 4 = ☐								
14 ÷ 7 = ☐								
5 x ☐ = 15								
27 ÷ ☐ = 3								
16 divided by 8 = ☐								
3 x ☐ = 15								
9 multiplied by 3 = ☐								
☐ x 2 = 14								
18 ÷ 9 = ☐								
15 ÷ ☐ = 3								
8 x ☐ = 16								
16 divided by 4 equals ☐								

Use this space for your notes and working out

Recap 20 - 30 facts

For this section, you need to read out the whole statement,

For example, $20 \div 10 = \square$

You say $20 \div 10 = 2$

Read out the following statements:

$20 \div 10 = \square$									
$3 \times \square = 24$									
4 multiplied by 6 equals $\square$									
$27 \div 3 = \square$									
5 times 5 equals $\square$									
$10 \times \square = 20$									
$21 \div 7 = \square$									

Recap

For this section, you need to read out the whole statement,

For example, $81 \div \square = 9$

You say $81 \div 9 = 9$

Read out the following statements:

$81 \div \square = 9$									
$72 \div 8 = \square$									
63 divided by 9 = $\square$									
$36 \div 6 = \square$									
$30 \div \square = 10$									
8 multiplied by 7 = $\square$									
$9 \times \square = 63$									

Use this space for your notes and working out

Fact Families

Write in the facts that link with the family of numbers. Write a different fact in each box.

24 6 4

5 20 4

7 14 2

4 16 4

18 2 9

6 18 3

Use this space
for your notes
and working out

Extended Problems

You can use the facts you know to help you work out other types of problems.

These problems include addition or subtraction, as well as multiplication or division.

With these problems you must always work out the multiplication or division part first.

For example,

$2 \times 10 + 1 = \boxed{}$

$2 \times 10 = 20$

$20 + 1 = \boxed{}$

You say $2 \times 10 + 1 = 21$

Read out the following statements:

$2 \times 10 + 1 = \boxed{}$	
$9 \times 3 + 3 = \boxed{}$	
$24 \div 8 + 2 = \boxed{}$	
$7 \times 3 - 2 = \boxed{}$	
$28 \div 7 + 1 = \boxed{}$	
$6 \times 4 + \boxed{} = 25$	
$5 \times 4 + 3 = \boxed{}$	
$25 \div 5 + \boxed{} = 6$	
$3 \times 9 - 2 = \boxed{}$	
$7 \times 4 + \boxed{} = 30$	
$3 \times 9 + 1 = \boxed{}$	
$10 \times 2 - \boxed{} = 18$	

The final facts to be introduced are:

$4 \times 2 = 8$	$3 \times 2 = 6$	$3 \times 4 = 12$	$6 \times 2 = 12$	$5 \times 2 = 10$
$2 \times 4 = 8$	$2 \times 3 = 6$	$4 \times 3 = 12$	$2 \times 6 = 12$	$2 \times 5 = 10$
$8 \div 2 = 4$	$6 \div 2 = 3$	$12 \div 4 = 3$	$12 \div 2 = 6$	$10 \div 2 = 5$
$8 \div 4 = 2$	$6 \div 3 = 2$	$12 \div 3 = 4$	$12 \div 6 = 2$	$10 \div 5 = 2$

$2 \times 2 = 4$	$3 \times 3 = 9$
$4 \div 2 = 2$	$9 \div 3 = 3$

Perform with Times Tables

For this section, you need to read out the whole statement,

For example,

$5 \times 2 = \Box$

You say $5 \times 2 = 10$

Remember, you need to get three consecutive ticks

Read out the following statements:

$5 \times 2 = \Box$	
$\Box \times 3 = 6$	
$3 \times 4 = \Box$	
$2 \times \Box = 4$	
$10 \div 2 = \Box$	
$6 \times 2 = \Box$	
8 divided by 2 equals $\Box$	
$9 \div 3 = \Box$	
$12 \div 4 = \Box$	
12 divided by 2 = $\Box$	
$6 \div \Box = 3$	
$2 \times 4 = \Box$	

Recap grid

Use this grid to put in any questions you have found difficult so far.

You can put in the questions you found hard or you can make up your own.

Remember, you need to get three consecutive ticks

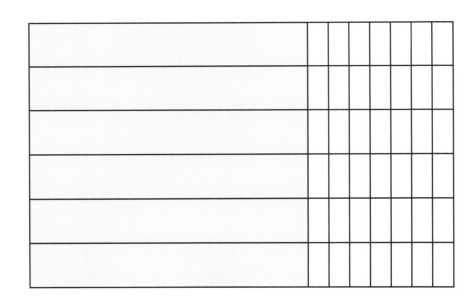

Perform with Times Tables

For this section, you need to read out the whole statement,

For example,

$4 \times 2 = \square$

You say $4 \times 2 = 8$

Remember, you need to get three consecutive ticks

Read out the following statements:

$4 \times 2 = \square$									
$6 \div \square = 2$									
$\square \times 5 = 10$									
$4 \times 3 = \square$									
$3 \times 3 = \square$									
$12 \div 6 = \square$									
$10 \div \square = 2$									
$3 \times \square = 6$									
4 divided by 2 equals $\square$									
$\square \times 6 = 12$									
$8 \div \square = 2$									
$12 \div 3 = \square$									

Fact Families

Write in the facts that link with the family of numbers. Write a different fact in each box.

16 2 8

| |
| |
| |
| |

15 5 3

| |
| |
| |
| |

5 2 10

| |
| |
| |
| |

6 12 2

| |
| |
| |
| |

4 3 12

| |
| |
| |
| |

3 9 3

| |
| |

Extended Problems

You can use the facts you know to help you work out other types of problems.

These problems include addition or subtraction, as well as multiplication or division.

With these problems you must always work out the multiplication or division part first.

For example,

$5 \times 2 + 1 = \square$

$5 \times 2 = 10$

$\qquad 10 + 1 = \square$

You say $5 \times 2 + 1 = 11$

Read out the following statements:

$5 \times 2 + 1 = \square$	
$15 \div 3 - 1 = \square$	
$16 \div 4 + \square = 5$	
$6 \times 2 + 3 = \square$	
$2 \times 7 - \square = 10$	
$8 \times 2 + \square = 18$	
$3 \times 5 - 2 = \square$	
$9 \div 3 + \square = 5$	
$2 \times 4 + 3 = \square$	
$3 \times 2 - \square = 1$	
$4 \times 4 + 4 = \square$	
$10 \div 2 + 5 = \square$	

Multiplying by 1 and 0

Multiplying by 1

When you multiply a number by 1, it is the same as saying '1 lot of the number'.

So 9 x 1 is the same as 9 lots of 1 = 9

Also, 1 x 9 = 1 lot of 9 = 9

Multiplying by 0

When you multiply a number by 0, it is the same as saying 'zero lots of the number'.

So 7 x 0 is the same as 7 lots of 0 = 0

Also, 0 x 7 = 0 lots of 7 = 0

Perform with Times Tables

For this section, you need to read out the whole statement,

For example,

$1 \times 9 = \square$

You say $1 \times 9 = 9$

Remember, you need to get three consecutive ticks

Read out the following statements:

$1 \times 9 = \square$							
$4 \times 1 = \square$							
$7 \times 0 = \square$							
$6 \times \square = 6$							
$3 \times \square = 0$							
$0 \times 8 = \square$							
$1 \times \square = 2$							
$\square \times 5 = 0$							
$\square \times 10 = 10$							
$2 \times 0 = \square$							
$4 \times \square = 0$							
$9 \times 1 = \square$							

Dividing using 1

Dividing by 1

When you divide a number by 1, it is the same as saying 'how many 1s will go into the number'.

So $9 \div 1$ is the same as saying how many 1s will divide into 9

$9 \div 1 = 9$

Dividing into 1

It is worth noting that 'dividing by 1' is different to 'dividing into 1'.

For example,
$1 \div 2$ means sharing '1 into 2'.

$1 \div 2 = \frac{1}{2}$.

This book will not cover dividing into 1 in any detail.

Recap

For this section, you need to read out the whole statement,

For example, $9 \times 9 = \square$

You say $9 \times 9 = 81$

Read out the following statements:

$9 \times 9 = \square$							
$42 \div 7 = \square$							
$5 \times 7 + \square = 38$							
$28 \div \square = 7$							
$9 \times 3 + 2 = \square$							
$8 \times \square = 80$							
$7 \times \square = 56$							
$63 \div 9 + \square = 10$							
$9 \times 5 = \square$							
$4 \times \square = 36$							
$24 \div \square = 6$							
$3 \times 5 + \square = 20$							

Recap

For this section, you need to read out the whole statement,

For example, $81 \div \square = 9$

You say $81 \div 9 = 9$

Read out the following statements:

$81 \div \square = 9$								
$9 \times \square = 72$								
$7 \times \square = 63$								
$56 \div \square = 8$								
$6 \times 6 + 4 = \square$								
$49 \div \square = 7$								
$3 \times 3 = \square$								
$8 \div 2 = \square$								
$9 \times 3 - 4 = \square$								
$8 \times 2 = \square$								
$32 \div \square = 4$								
$10 \times 10 = \square$								

Recap grid

Use this grid to put in any questions you have found difficult so far.

You can put in the questions you found hard or you can make up your own.

Remember, you need to get three consecutive ticks

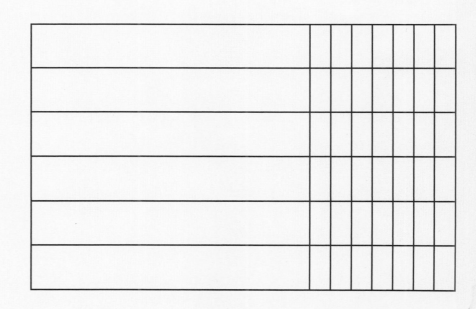

Congratulations!

You have now completed Times Tables

Well Done
You should be
proud of yourself